Guest Spot

JAZZ
Playalong *for* Flute

WISE PUBLICATIONS
London/New York/Paris/Sydney/Copenhagen/Madrid

Fingering Guide

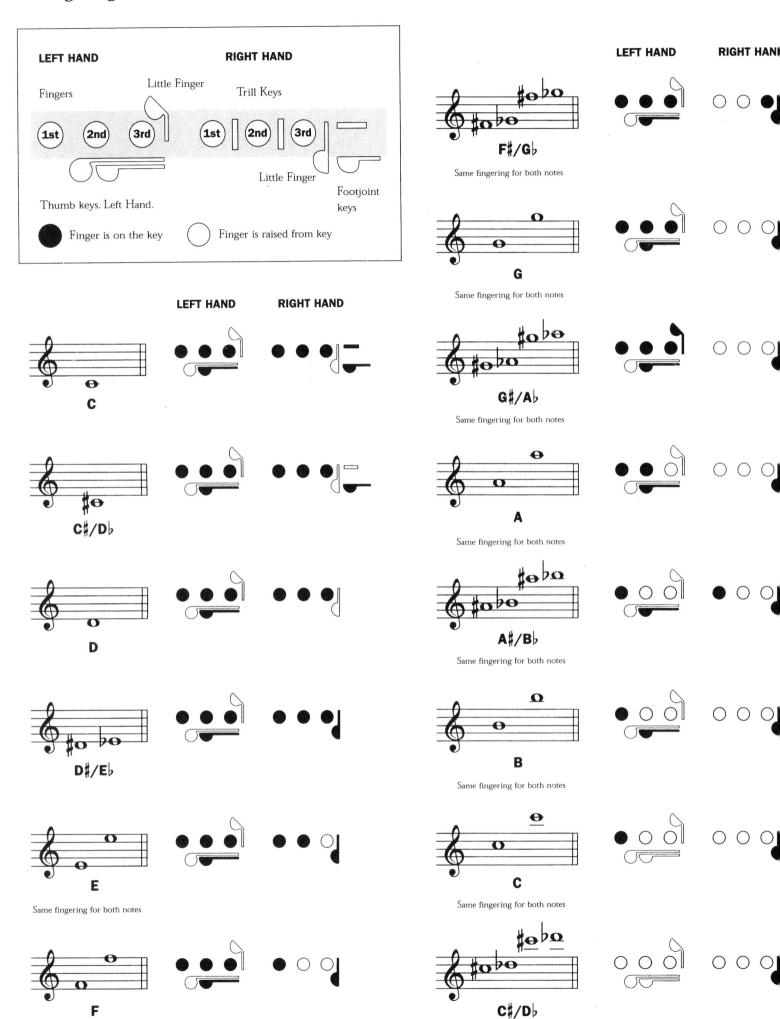

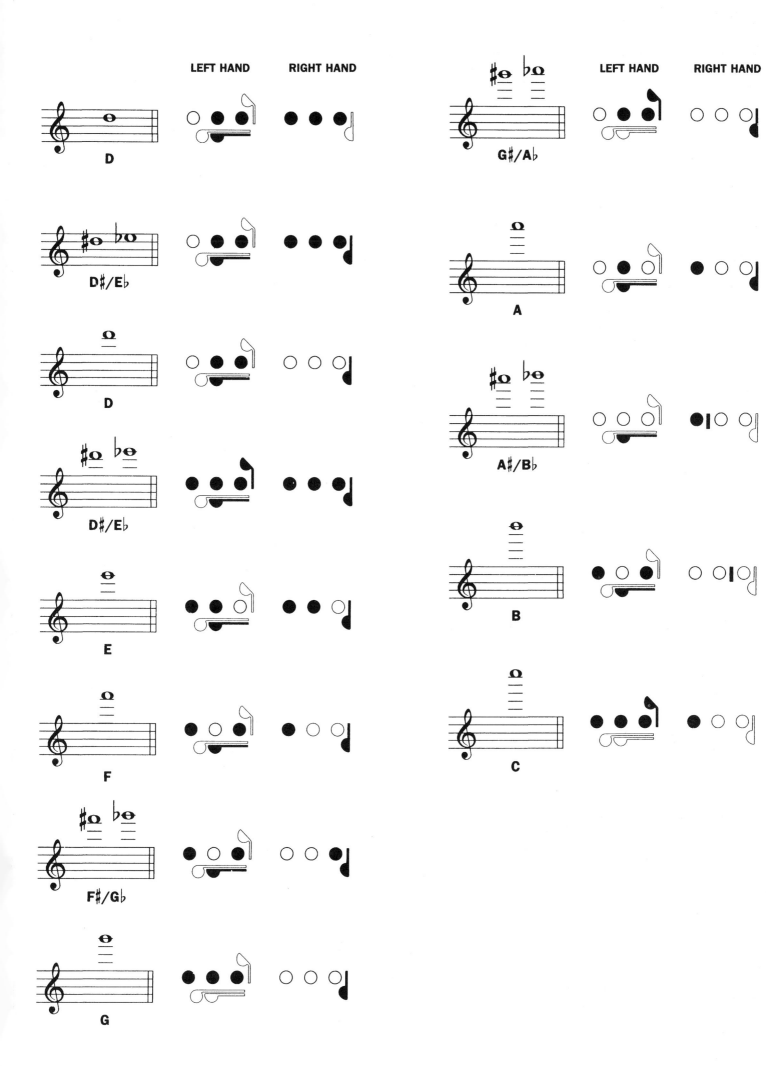

A Night In Tunisia

Music by Frank Paparelli & John 'Dizzy' Gillespie

To Coda ⊕

D.S. (with repeat) al Coda

CODA

Bernie's Tune

By Bernie Miller

Fast ($\quad$ = 104)

D. 𝄋 *(with repeat) al Coda*

𝄌 **CODA**

Fly Me To The Moon
(In Other Words)

Words & Music by Bart Howard

Medium fast (♩ = 88)

To Coda

D.S. (with repeat) al Coda

7

CODA

One Note Samba
(Samba De Uma Nota So)

By Antonio Carlos Jobim

Bossa nova (♩ = 76)

D.S. al Coda

CODA

Opus One

Words & Music by Sy Oliver

Medium fast ($\quad = 84$)

(sim.)

D.$\mathsection$ (with repeat) al Coda

$\oplus$ **CODA**

Satin Doll

Music by Duke Ellington & Billy Strayhorn

Slightly Out Of Tune
(Desafinado)

By Antonio Carlos Jobim

Bossa nova (♩ = 76)

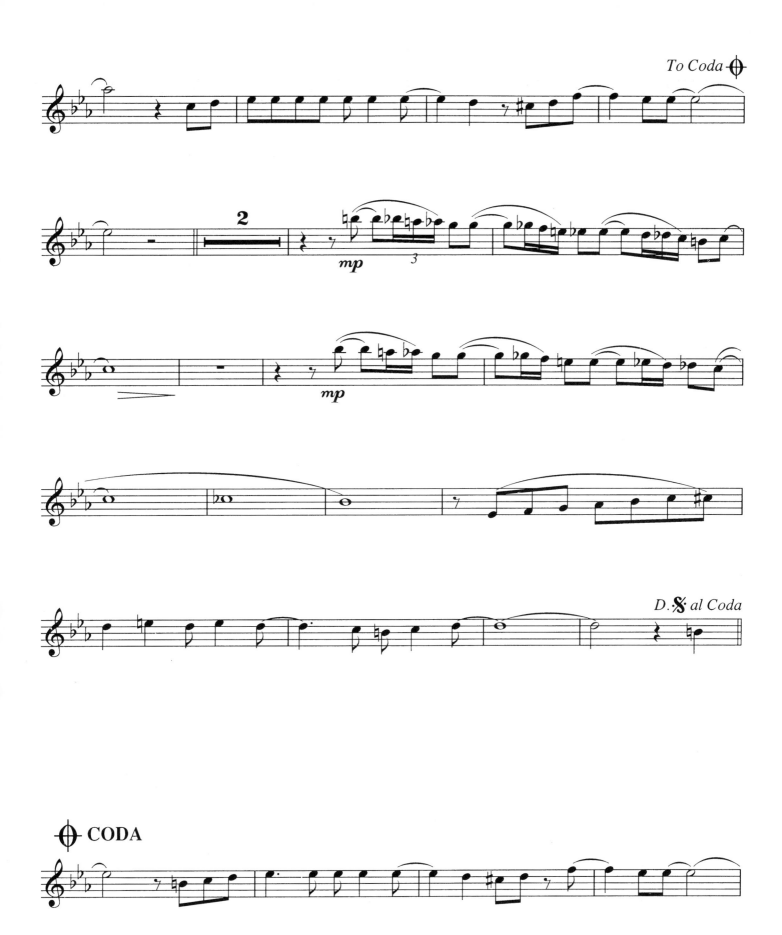

D.𝄋 al Coda

⊕ **CODA**

rall.

Straight No Chaser

By Thelonious Monk

Medium fast ($\quad = 80$)

D.%*(with repeat) al Coda*

CODA

Take The 'A' Train

Words & Music by Billy Strayhorn

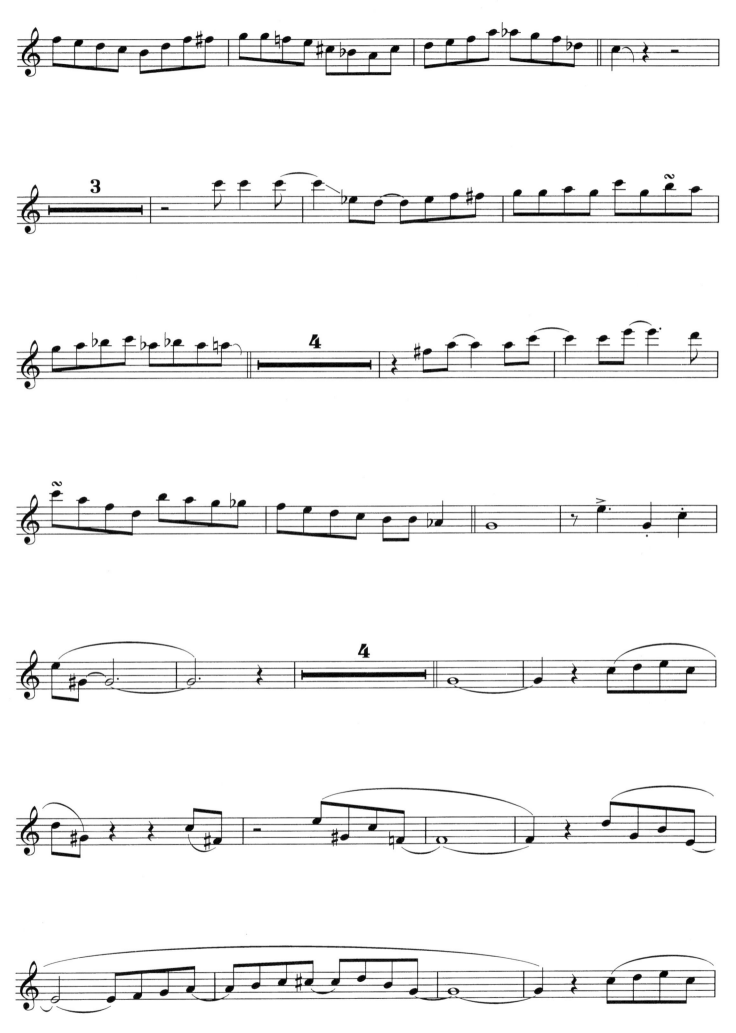

D.S. *(with repeats) al Coda*

CODA

Yardbird Suite

By Charlie Parker

D. 𝄌 *(with repeat) al Coda*

𝄌 **CODA**

11/02 (45808)

Exclusive Distributors:
Music Sales Limited
8/9 Frith Street, London W1V 5TZ, England.
Music Sales Pty Limited
120 Rothschild Avenue, Rosebery, NSW 2018, Australia.

Order No. AM941710
ISBN 0-7119-6252-9
This book © Copyright 1998 by Wise Publications.

Book design by Michael Bell Design.
Compiled by Peter Evans.
Music arranged by Jack Long & Paul Honey.
Music processed by Enigma Music Production Services.
Cover photography by George Taylor.

Printed in the United Kingdom by
Page Bros. Limited, Norwich, Norfolk.

CD recorded by Passionhouse Music.
Instrumental solos by John Whelan.
Produced by Paul Honey.

Your Guarantee of Quality:
As publishers, we strive to produce every book to
the highest commercial standards.
The music has been freshly engraved and the book has been
carefully designed to minimise awkward page turns and
to make playing from it a real pleasure.
Particular care has been given to specifying acid-free, neutral-sized
paper made from pulps which have not been elemental chlorine bleached.
This pulp is from farmed sustainable forests and was
produced with special regard for the environment.
Throughout, the printing and binding have been planned to
ensure a sturdy, attractive publication which should give years of enjoyment.
If your copy fails to meet our high standards,
please inform us and we will gladly replace it.

Music Sales' complete catalogue describes thousands of
titles and is available in full colour sections by subject,
direct from Music Sales Limited.
Please state your areas of interest and send a
cheque/postal order for £1.50 for postage to:
Music Sales Limited, Newmarket Road, Bury St. Edmunds, Suffolk IP33 3YB.